START WRITI
A writing course for Arab students

C000299593

Richard Harrison

CANFORD PUBLISHING

www. canfordpublishing.com

Canford Publishing
London, UK

www. canfordpublishing.com

© Canford Publishing Limited, 2014

Published by Canford Publishing. All rights reserved. No part of this publication may be reproduced, stored in a retrieval system, or transmitted in any form and by any means, without prior permission in writing by Canford Publishing.

First published: 2014

Printed in Oman by Mazoon Printing, Publishing and Advertising (L.L.C).

ISBN: 978-99969-806-0-2

Reg. No: 299/2014

Contents

To the Student

عزيزي الطالب

Welcome to Start Writing, a new writing course for the Arab World.

Who is Start Writing for?

Start Writing is for those students who are not familiar with English letters and numbers and those students who would like more practice in forming the shapes.

What is Start Writing?

The main aims of Start Writing are:

- to introduce and practise the numbers 0 - 10

- to introduce and practise the letters of the alphabet (large and small letters)

Start Writing also presents a number of useful everyday phrases for use in conversation - for example: "My names's....", "What's the time?", Where are you from?"

It also introduces some useful vocabulary. Many of the words are similar to words used in Arabic - for example: jacket, passport and video. You may be surprised. You already know more English words than you think!

Finally, Start Writing also shows you how to use punctuation in English sentences and when to use capital letters (A,B,C, ...) and when to use small letters (a,b,c, ...).

How to use Start Writing

You can use the book in class with a teacher or working on your own at home. It is important to follow the instructions for forming a letter or a number.

To help you draw the shapes correctly you are given sets of four lines to write on.

أهلا بك إلى الكتاب الجديد "Start Writing" الموجّه إلى العالم العربي.

ما هي الشريحة التي يستهدفها الكتاب؟

يستهدف الكتاب الطلبة الذين ليس لديهم إلمام بالحروف والأرقام في اللغة الإنجليزية بالإضافة إلى أولئك الراغبين في التدرب بشكل أكبر على رسم أشكال هذه الحروف والأرقام.

ما هو كتاب "Start Writing"؟

يهدف الكتاب إلى تحقيق الآتي:

– التعريف بالأرقام من 0-10 وتدريب الطلبة عليها.

– التعريف بالحروف الأبجدية في اللغة الإنجليزية وتدريب الطلبة على كتابتها (الحروف الكبيرة والصغيرة).

يقدم كتاب "Start Writing" عدداً من العبارات المفيدة التي تُستخدم المحادثات اليومية مثل : .... ،My name's What's the time? Where are you from كما يتضمن عدداً من المفردات المفيدة شبيهة بتلك المستخدمة في العربية مثل jacket، passport، video. وقد تكتشف أنك تعرف كلمات إنجليزية أكثر مما كنت تظن.

وأخيراً، يوضح كتاب "Start Writing" لك كيفية نطق الجمل الإنجليزية والحالات التي يجب أن تستخدم فيها الحروف الأبجدية الكبيرة (A،B،C) والحروف الصغيرة (a،b،c).

كيف يمكنك استخدام كتاب "Start Writing"؟

يُمكِن اعتِماد الكتاب في الصفّ مع وُجود مُدرِّس ، أو يُمكِنك الدَّرس به في البَيت مِن دون مُدرِّس . ومِن الأهَمِّيَّة بِمكان اتِّباع التَّعليمات لِلتوصُّل إلى الكِتابة الصَّحيحة لِلحُروف والأرقام .

ولِمُساعَدتك على رسَم الأشْكال بِالطَّريقة الصَّحيحة هُناك أربَعة أسطُر لِلكِتابة .

The numbers and most of the letters rest on the solid line.

إنَّ كُلَّ الأرقام ومُعظَم الحُروف تَكون قاعِدتها على السَّطر الثَّخين .

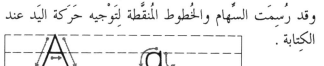

Arrows and dotted lines show you how to make the shapes of the numbers and letters.

وقد رُسِمَت السِّهام والخُطوط المُنقَّطة لتَوْجيه حَرَكة اليَد عند الكِتابة .

Some small letters have "tails" which extend below the solid line.

وتَجدر المُلاحَظة أنَّ لِبَعض الحُروف الصَّغيرة ذَيْلا يَنزل تحت السَّطْر الثَّخين .

What will I be able to do by the end of Start Writing?

ماذا ستستفيد من كتاب "Start Writing"؟

There are 26 capital letters (A to Z) and 26 small letters (a to z) as well as the numbers 0 to 9. By the end of Start Writing you should be able to write them all clearly. You should also be able to join letters so as to write words, including your own name, the name of your city and the name of your country.

ستتمكن من كتابة الحروف الكبيرة (A-Z) والحروف الصغيرة (a-z) والأعداد من 0-10 بشكل واضح، كما سيتمكن من دمج الحروف مع بعضها لتكوين كلمات بما فيها اسمك واسم مدينتك واسم دولتك .

My name's Samira. I'm from Aswan in Egypt.

You will also be able to greet people in English and ask and answer a few simple questions. Good luck!

وسيكون بمقدورك تحية الأخرين باللغة الإنجليزية بالإضافة إلى طرحٍ وإجابة بعض الأسئلة البسيطة. حظًا موفقاً!

1   Left to right   مِن اليَسار إلى اليَمين

Left

Right

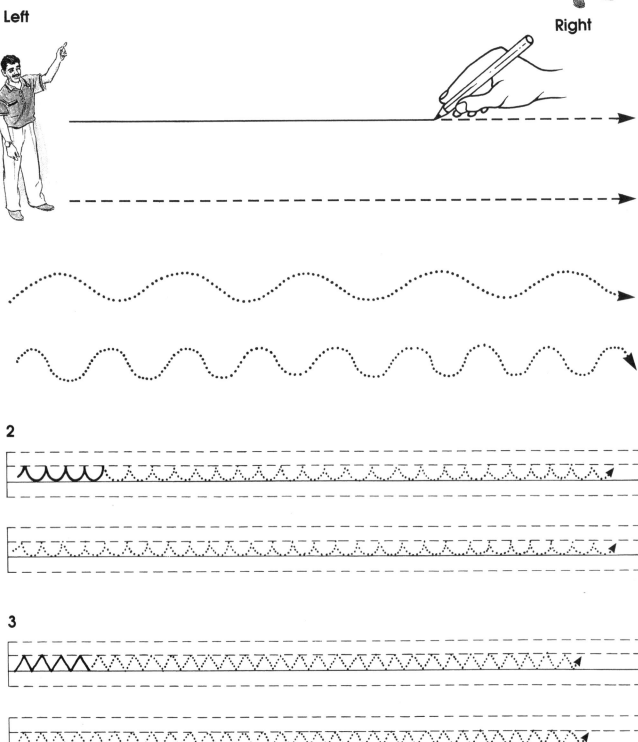

2

3

4

Left, right, left, right.

5 Numbers: 0, 1, 2, 3 الأَرْقام: ٠، ١، ٢، ٣

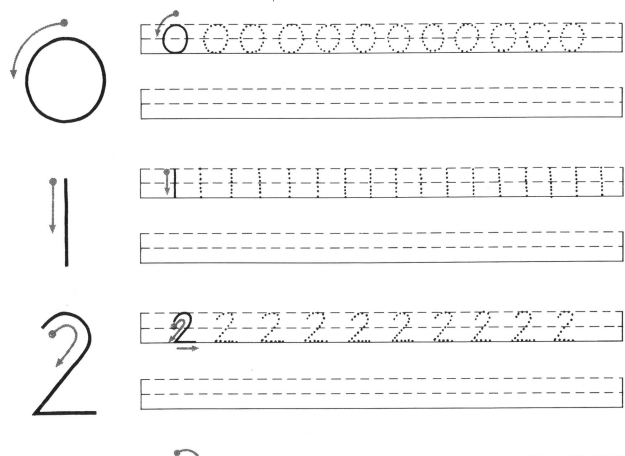

1 Numbers: 4, 5, 6 الأَرْقام: ٤، ٥، ٦

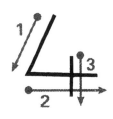
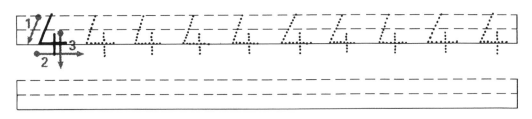

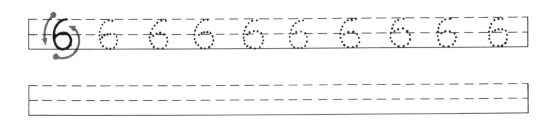

2 Match مائِل

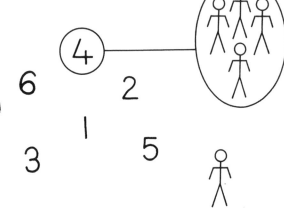

6

2

1

5

3

3 Telephone numbers أَرقام الهاتِف

4 Listen and write اِسْتَمِعْ واكْتُبْ

Telephone numbers

5 Write the licence number اُكْتُبْ رَقْم لَوْحَة السَّيّارَة

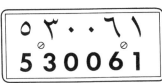

530061

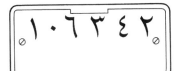

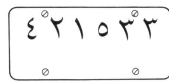

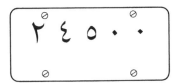

1 Numbers: 7, 8, 9 ٩ ،٨ ،٧ :الأَرْقام

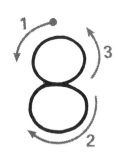

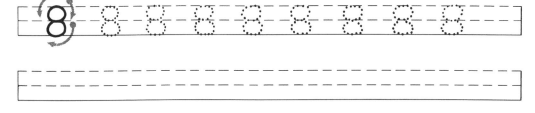

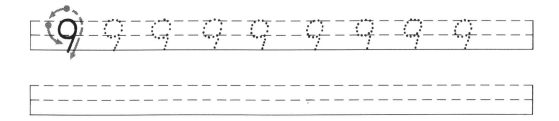

2   Match the numbers ماثِلْ بينَ الأَرْقام

0	7	3	0	5	4	2	0	8	1	4	0	9	7	6	0
1	6	1	7	8	0	1	3	5	4	9	8	6	2	1	7
2	8	4	6	2	7	9	2	3	0	4	2	1	6	9	5
3	6	5	3	8	0	1	3	7	5	3	8	4	1	3	2
4	2	4	9	1	3	4	6	2	4	7	6	1	5	4	9
5	8	6	0	5	1	8	4	3	5	9	5	3	1	2	5
6	2	0	7	3	6	0	5	6	7	2	1	6	4	8	3
7	9	5	0	2	7	3	7	1	4	7	5	0	2	7	6
8	2	4	1	8	5	1	0	8	9	3	8	6	0	2	7
9	3	9	5	2	1	4	9	0	8	7	9	1	6	9	2

3 Write اُكْتُب

4 Listen and write اِسْتَمِعْ واكتُبْ

5 Write the licence number اُكْتُب رَقْم لَوْحَة السَّيَّارَة

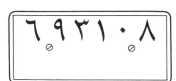

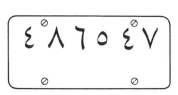

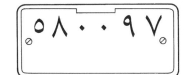

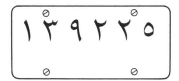

8

1 A B C

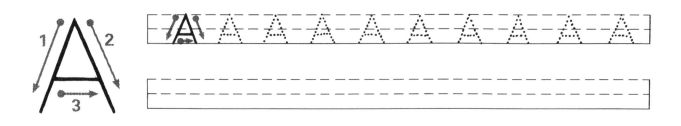

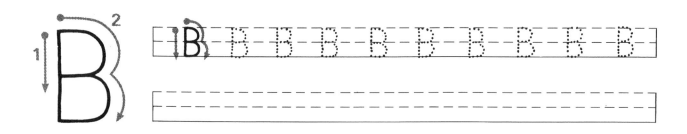

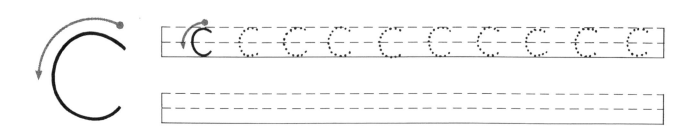

2 Match مائِلْ

A	C	A	B	B	A	C	A	C	B	A	C	B	C	A	B	C
B	A	C	C	B	A	B	A	C	B	C	B	A	C	A	C	B
C	B	C	B	A	C	B	A	A	C	C	B	A	B	B	C	A

3 Listen and put an X اِسْتَمِعْ وضَعْ عَلامة ×

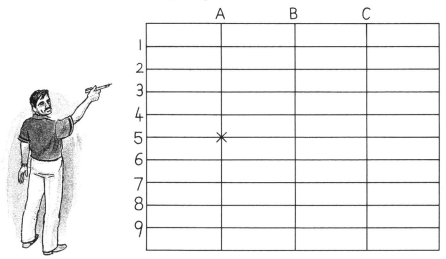

	A	B	C
1			
2			
3			
4			
5	×		
6			
7			
8			
9			

4 Listen and write اِسْتَمِعْ واكْتُبْ

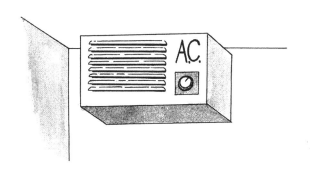

1 D E F

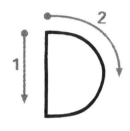 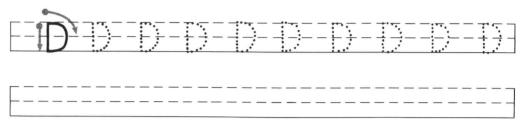

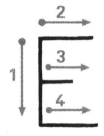 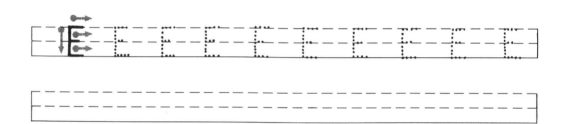

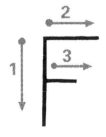 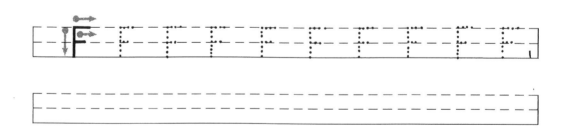

2 Match مَائِلْ

D	A	F	C	D	E	B	D	C	A	D	E	D	B	F	A	C
E	B	E	F	C	A	E	B	D	F	E	E	A	C	D	F	B
F	C	A	F	C	A	B	F	D	E	F	B	C	F	E	A	B

3 Match مائِل

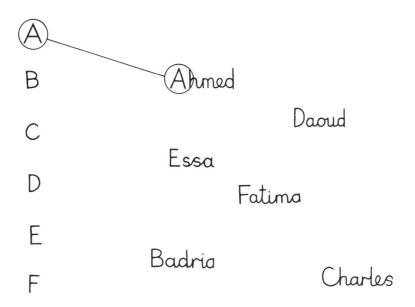

A   Ahmed

B

C   Daoud

        Essa

D   Fatima

E

      Badria

F   Charles

4 Write اُكْتُب

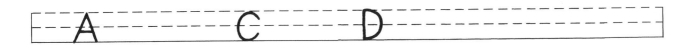

A   C   D

5 Listen and write اِسْتَمِعْ واكْتُب

5 B.D.

1 G H I

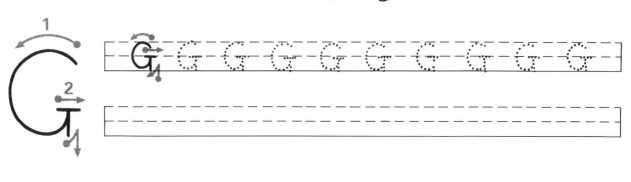

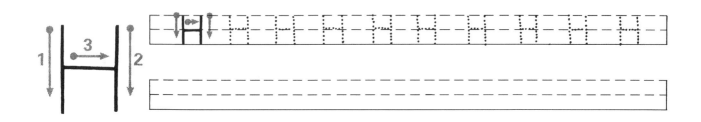

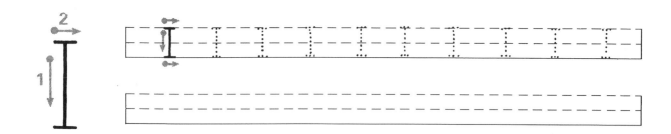

2   Match مائِلْ

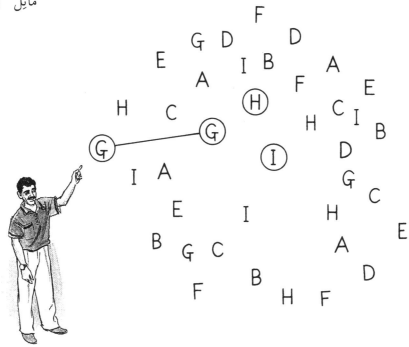

3   Listen and write اِسْتمِعْ واكْتُبْ

4   Say قُلْ

1 J K L

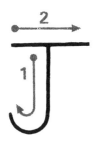
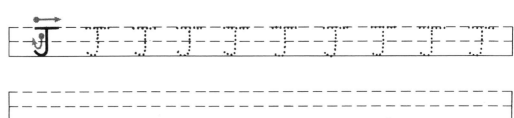

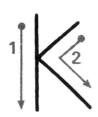
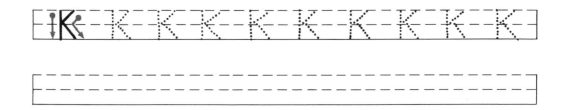

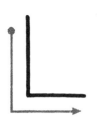

2   Match مائِلْ

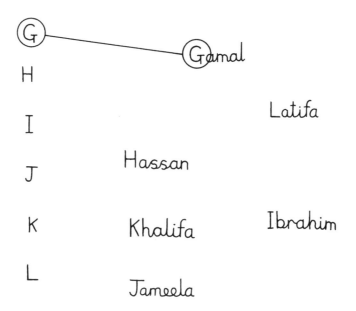

G   Gamal

H

I   Latifa

J   Hassan

K   Khalifa   Ibrahim

L   Jameela

3   Write اُكْتُبْ

A   C   E F   H   J   L

4   Listen and write اِسْتَمِعْ واكْتُبْ

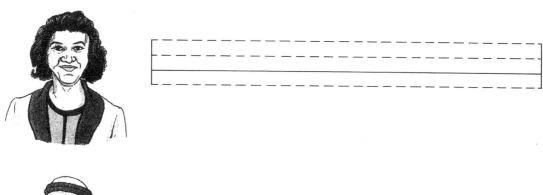

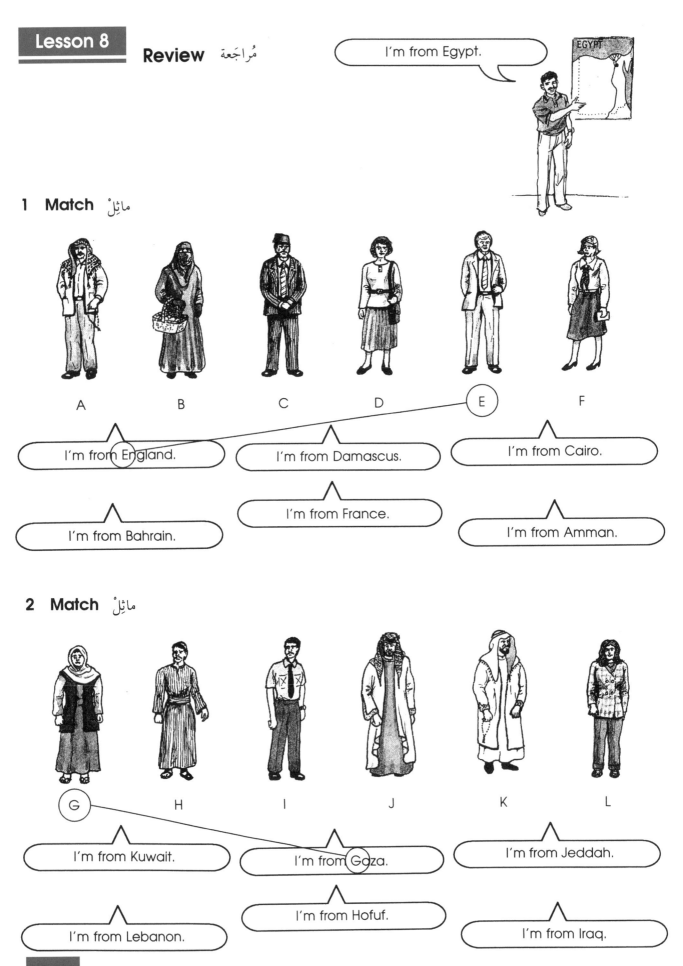

I'm from Egypt.

1 Match مائِلْ

A B C D E F

I'm from England. I'm from Damascus. I'm from Cairo.

I'm from France.

I'm from Bahrain. I'm from Amman.

2 Match مائِلْ

G H I J K L

I'm from Kuwait. I'm from Gaza. I'm from Jeddah.

I'm from Hofuf.

I'm from Lebanon. I'm from Iraq.

3 Match مائِلْ

A	B	K	F	<u>A</u>	G	I	H	A	L	E	A	B	H	K	F	A
B	E	A	J	B	I	D	B	C	E	G	B	I	F	D	B	G
C	F	G	L	C	I	G	C	K	H	B	D	C	G	B	C	K
D	B	D	E	I	A	D	F	B	D	C	J	G	L	D	E	C
E	F	I	J	E	H	B	L	K	E	I	J	E	L	F	B	E
F	B	A	K	H	F	D	E	F	B	G	D	L	F	A	E	F
G	K	C	B	G	A	D	B	G	J	L	E	C	G	A	G	D
H	I	A	H	L	K	H	J	E	A	D	K	E	H	H	I	B
I	E	B	I	A	C	I	J	L	C	I	D	E	L	K	J	I
J	L	J	A	I	J	H	A	I	J	C	B	E	J	L	B	H
K	A	E	K	F	H	J	K	C	A	K	E	H	A	K	L	J
L	F	L	I	D	L	E	C	L	A	I	J	K	B	E	J	L

4 Listen and write اِسْتَمِعْ واكْتُبْ

---

5 Listen and write اِسْتَمِعْ واكْتُبْ

	Flight Number
Damascus	_ _ _ _ _ _ _
Cairo	_ _ _ _ _ _ _
Jeddah	_ _ _ _ _ _ _
Kuwait	_ _ _ _ _ _ _
Bahrain	_ _ _ _ _ _ _

1 MNO

My name's Mary.

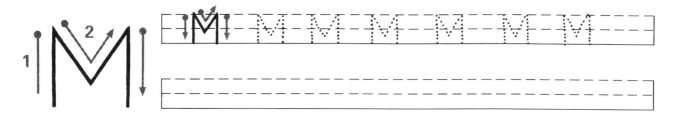

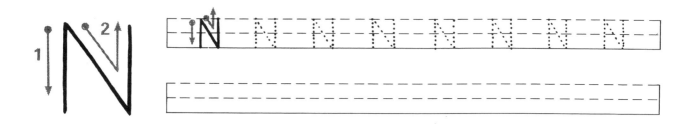

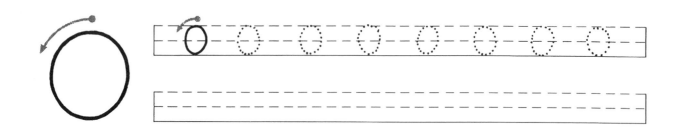

2 Match ماثِل

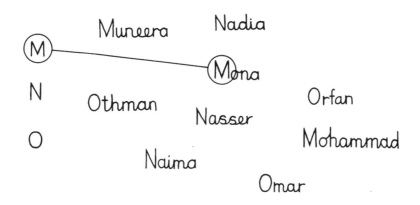

M —— Muneera Nadia
M⊘na
N Othman Orfan
Nasser
O Mohammad
Naima
Omar

3 Say قُلْ

A

┌──────────────────────────┐
│ Hello. My name's . . . . │
└──────────────────────────┘

B

┌────────────────────────────────┐
│ Hello, ... My name's . . . . │
└────────────────────────────────┘

4 Say قُلْ

A H J K
B C D E G
F L M N
I

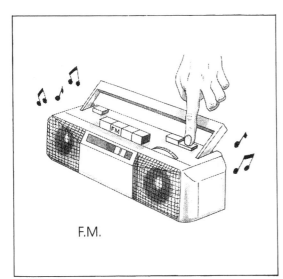

F.M.

20

1 P Q R

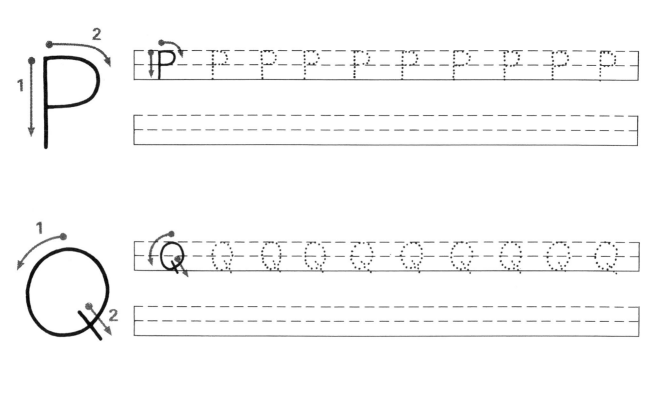

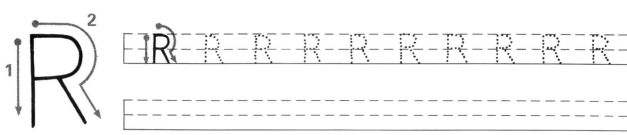

2 Match مائِلْ

M	K	H	F	<u>M</u>	P	N	A	B	M	C	D	M	F	N	M	H
N	C	E	N	L	K	H	M	B	N	D	M	I	A	N	M	K
O	O	D	B	C	Q	P	O	C	D	B	Q	O	C	O	P	Q
P	F	L	R	P	K	F	R	P	J	B	D	P	B	M	P	R
Q	O	A	Q	P	C	G	Q	O	B	R	Q	G	O	Q	G	H
R	K	J	M	R	P	F	K	R	J	A	R	P	O	F	K	R

3 Match مائِلْ

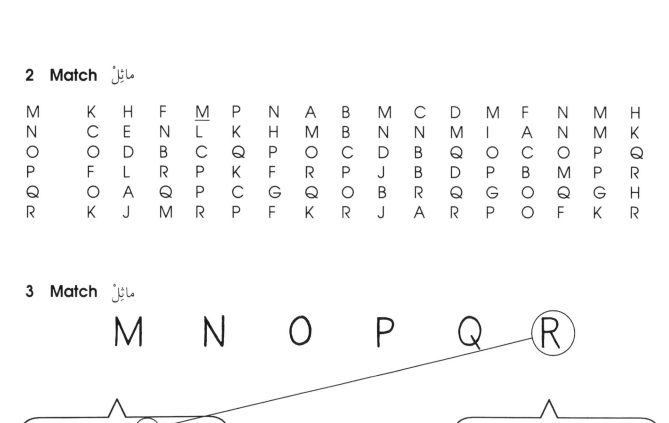

M   N   O   P   Q   R

My name's Rashid.

I'm from Oman.

I'm from Qatar

My name's Nadia.

I'm from Palestine.

My name's Mona.

4 Write اُكْتُبْ

B   C   E   G   I

J   M   O   R

5 Say قُلْ

P   B

M   N

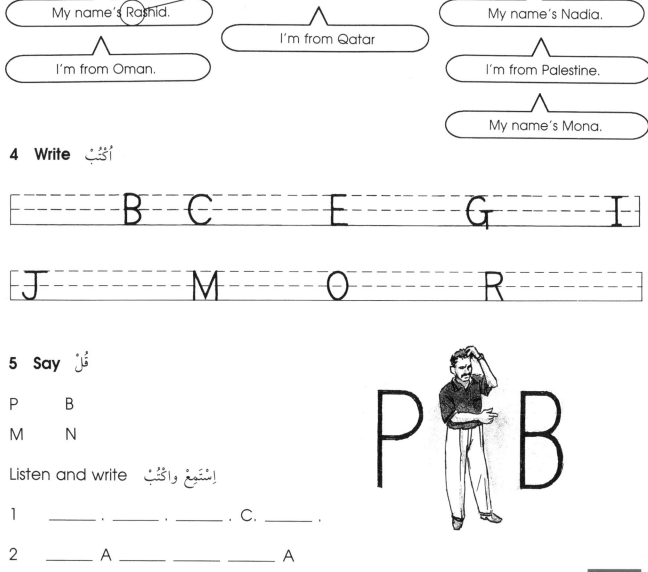

P B

Listen and write اِسْتَمِعْ واكْتُبْ

1 _____ . _____ . _____ . C. _____ .

2 _____ A _____ _____ _____ A

22

1 S T U

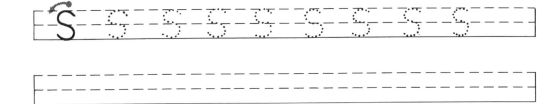

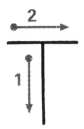
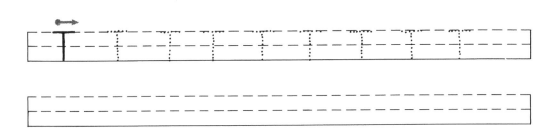

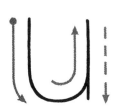

2 Match مائِلْ

```
S   B   P   S   E   C   D   E   S   R   Q   D   S   P   B   S   C
T   I   J   H   A   T   I   H   L   T   J   P   T   H   T   L   F
U   Q   C   U   J   D   B   U   A   L   G   Q   U   O   G   U   J
```

3 Match مائِلْ

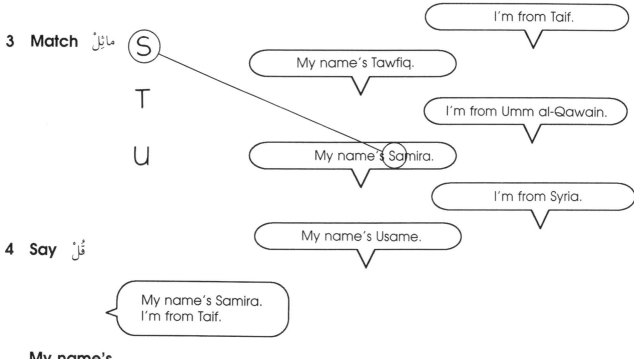

S

T

U

I'm from Taif.

My name's Tawfiq.

I'm from Umm al-Qawain.

My name's Samira.

I'm from Syria.

My name's Usame.

4 Say قُلْ

My name's Samira.
I'm from Taif.

My name's . . .
I'm from . . .

5 Listen and write اِسْتَمِعْ واكْتُبْ

U.A.E.

STOP

GO

Welcome!

1   V W

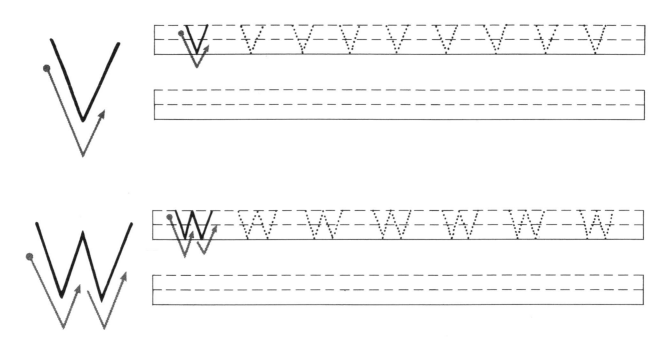

2   Match اُكْتُبْ

V	A	W	U	V	M	N	V	O	P	V	W	A	L	U	A	W	V
W	V	U	W	M	K	W	N	V	M	W	K	M	U	W	N	A	T

3   Listen and write اِسْتَمِعْ واكْتُبْ

4 Write اُكْتُبْ

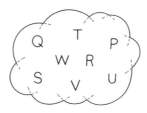

A B C D E F G H I J K L M N O

5 Write اُكْتُبْ

TV, BMW, VIP

_____

_____

I'm Ahmed. Welcome to Cairo!

CAIRO AIRPORT

My name's Waleed.

1 X Y Z

 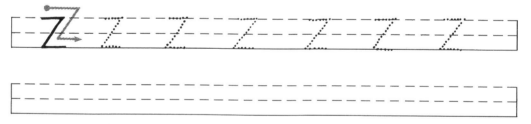

2 Match مائِل

X	Y	A	X̲	W	H	R	T	X	Y	V	X	W	B	X	Y	A
Y	V	W	Y̲	E	A	Y	K	V	S	A	Y	K	N	V	M	Y
Z	J	S	G	Z	S	T	E	Z	B	K	S	N	Z	V	Z	K

3 Write اُكْتُب

A ___ C ___ E ___ G ___ I ___ K ___

M ___ O ___ Q ___ S ___ U ___ W ___ Y ___

F   L   Z   B   R   N   D   X   V   P   H   T   J

4 Listen and write اِسْتَمِعْ واكْتُبْ

Review مُراجَعة

1 Capital letters ١ الحُروف الكَبيرة

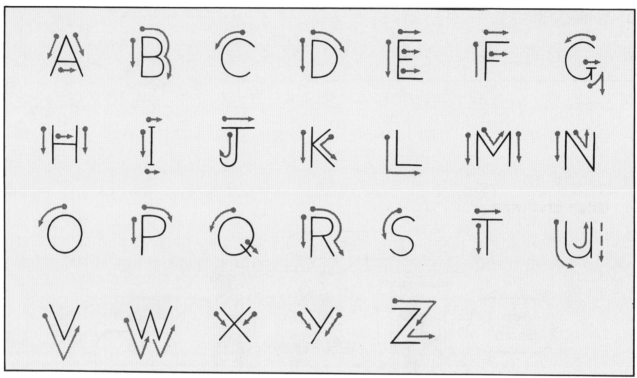

2 Numbers الأَرْقام

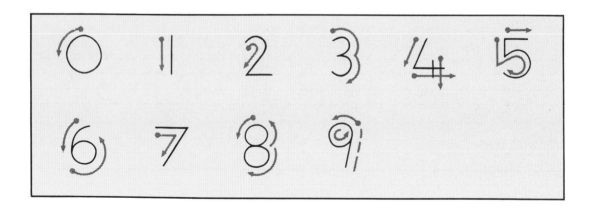

3 Say قُلْ

A	H	J	K			
B	C	D	E	G	P	T	V
F	L	M	N	S	X	Z
I	Y					
O						
Q	U	W				
R						

4 What is it? ما هو؟

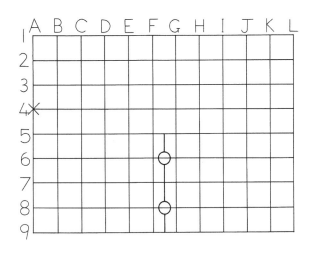

A4, B3, C2, D1, E1, F5, G5, H1, I1, J2,
K3, L4, K5, J4, I3, I9, D9, D3, C4, B5, A4.

5 What is it? ما هي؟

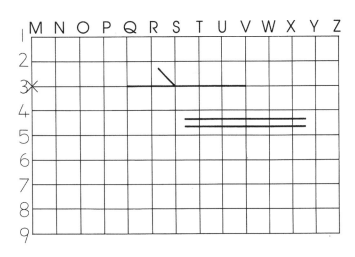

M3, Q3, R1, U1, V3, Y3, Z2, Z3,
Z6, X6, W7, V6, R6, Q7, P6, M6, M3.

1 A B C a b c

a a a a a a a a a a a a a

 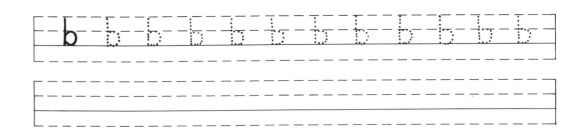

b b b b b b b b b b b b b

c c c c c c c c c c c c

2 Match مائِلْ

a   Abdullah, Bahrain, Salalah

b   Habiba, Abu Dhabi, Aqaba

c   Damascus, welcome, car

3 Write أُكْتُب

ab _ab_

cab _cab_

Look!	اُنْظُرْ!

A a   Amman,   Anwar,   and

B b   Balbek,   Habbib,   cab

C c   Cairo,   Charles,   welcome

1 **D E F   d e f**

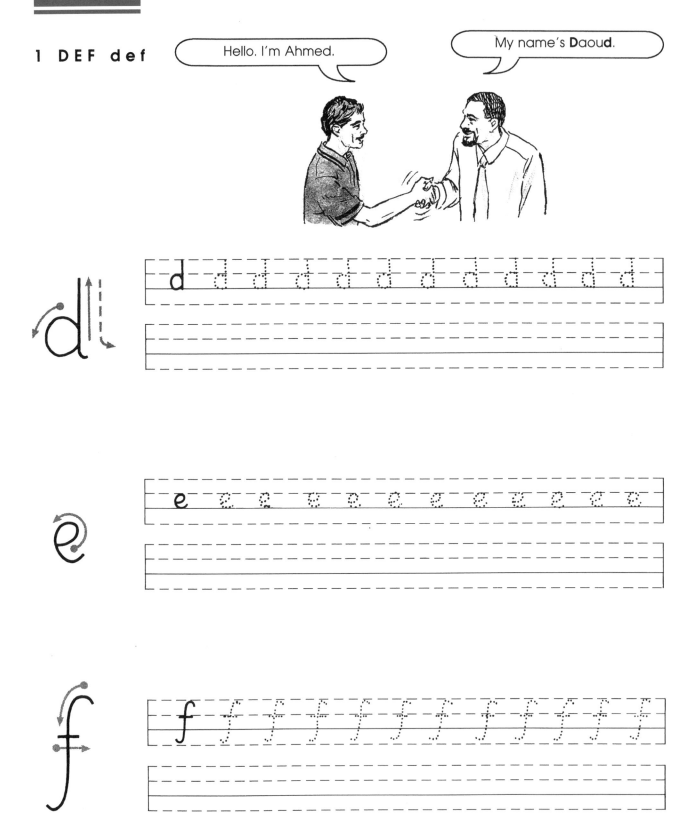

Hello. I'm Ahmed.

My name's **D**aou**d**.

d d d d d d d d d d d d d

e e e e e e e e e e e e

f f f f f f f f f f f f f

2 Match مائِل

d	Saeed, Riyadh, Jordan
e	Waleed, name, hello
f	Lateefa, Taif, from

3 Match مائِل

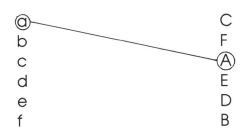

4 Write اُكْتُب

bed bed

bad bad

face face

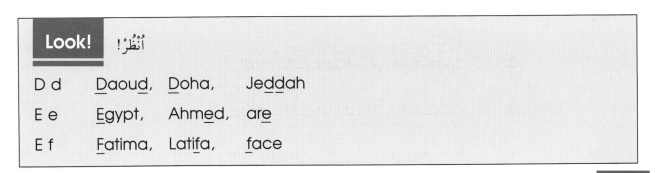

Look!	أُنْظُرْ!		
D d	Daoud,	Doha,	Jeddah
E e	Egypt,	Ahmed,	are
F f	Fatima,	Latifa,	face

1 G H I   g h i

 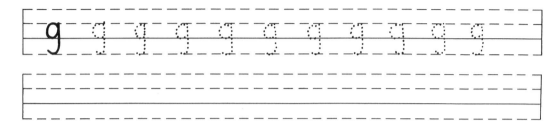

 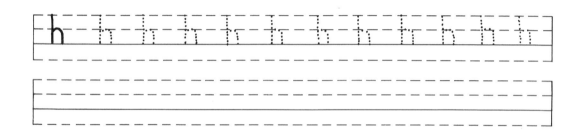

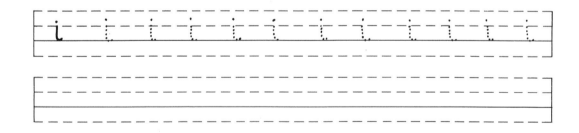

2 Match مائِل

g   George, Algeria, England

h   Salah, Sharjah, thanks

i   Ibrahim, Saudi Arabia, fine

3 Write اُكْتُبْ

big big

bag bag

head head

4 Write اُكْتُبْ

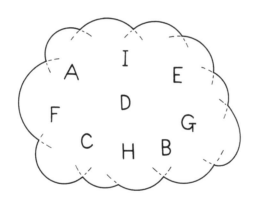

A I E
F D G
C H B

a __ b __ c __ d __ e __ f __ g __ h __ i __

Look!	اُنْظُرْ!

G g George, garage

H h Ahmed Hassan, happy

I i I'm from Irbid in Jordan.

1 J K L j k l

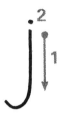

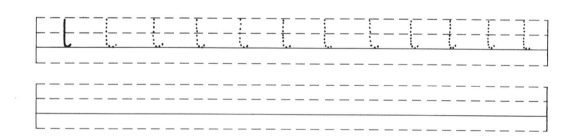

2 Match مائِل

j	Haji, Khadija, Sharjah
k	Kirkuk, Sheikh, thanks
l	Latifa, capital letter

3 Write أُكْتُبْ

jack jack

ball ball

Haji Haji

4 Match مائِلْ

j	b	d	a	j	i	k	b	f	h	c	j	e	j	a	g	i
k	h	k	b	h	j	a	k	l	c	d	k	i	j	e	f	k
l	l	a	c	l	d	b	l	f	a	h	g	e	i	l	k	j

Look!	اُنْظُرْ!

J j	<u>J</u>ordan,	Ha<u>j</u>i,	<u>j</u>eep
K k	<u>K</u>era<u>k</u>,	Ba<u>kk</u>er,	ja<u>ck</u>et
L l	<u>L</u>u<u>l</u>wa,	A<u>l</u>geria,	sma<u>ll</u> <u>l</u>etter

Review مُراجَعة

1 Match ماثِلْ

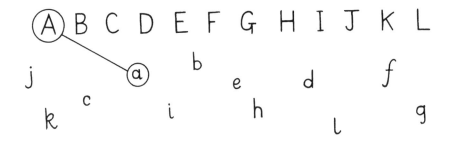

2 Write اُكْتُبْ

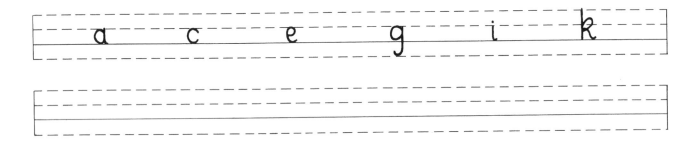

3 Write اُكْتُبْ

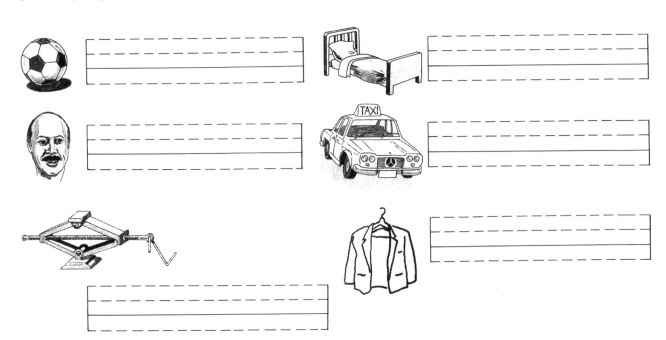

4 Listen and write اِسْتَمِعْ واكْتُبْ

Write small letters.

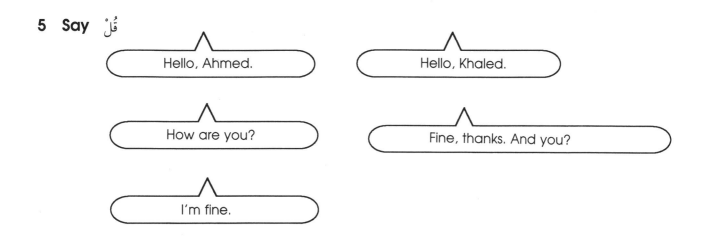

5 Say قُلْ

Hello, Ahmed.	Hello, Khaled.
How are you?	Fine, thanks. And you?
I'm fine.	

A
Hello, ...
How are you?
I'm fine.

B
Hello, ...
Fine, thanks. And you?

WORDS كَلِمات

| capital letter | حَرْف كَبير |
| small letter | حَرْف صَغير |

bad	سَيِّئ	bed	سَرير	car	سَيّارة	head	رَأْس
bag	مِحْفظة	big	كَبيرَ	face	وَجْه	jack	رافِعَة
ball	كُرَة	cab (taxi)	تَكْسي	goal	هَدَف	jacket	سُتْرة

1 M N O m n o

m m m m m m m m m m m m

n n n n n n n n n n n n

o o o o o o o o o o o o

2 Match مائِل

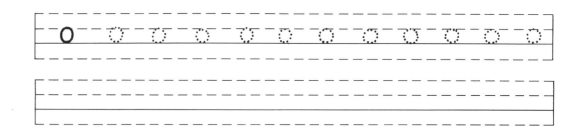

m   I'm from Dammam. My name's Fatima.

n   My name's Hannan. I'm from Lebanon.

o   Hello, Noor. How are you?

Look! اُنْظُرْ!

'm = am

I'm fine.	I am fine.
I'm Ali.	I am Ali.
I'm from Amman.	I am from Amman.

3 Write اُكْتُبْ

I'm fine   I am fine

man   and

no   not   not bad

book   good

Look! اُنْظُرْ!

M m   Mohammad, Muscat, man

N n   Nadia, Hannan, name

O o   Oman, Omar, Jordan, good

Lesson 21

1 **P Q R p q r**

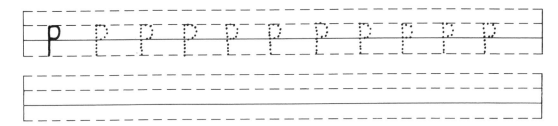

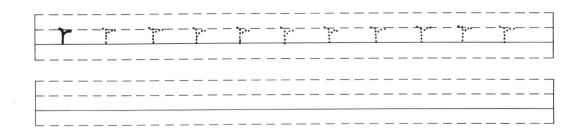

2 **Match** مائِلْ

p   Aleppo, pizza, passport

q   Aqaba, Tariq, queen

r   Morocco, Samira, recorder

3 Write أُكْتُب

 pen _pen_ radio _radio_

 car _car_ park _park_

are _are_ jeep _jeep_

No parking _No parking_

4 Write أُكْتُب

a   d   e   g   j   k   n   p   r

Look!	أُنْظُرْ!
P p	Pepsi, Petra, happy, pick-up, please
R r	Rashid, Jordan, birthday, car
Q q	Qatar, Abdul Qader, Iraq, Tawfiq

44

1 STU stu

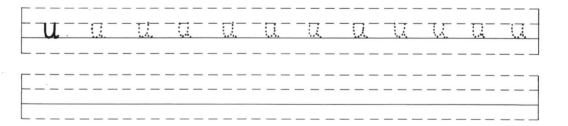

2 Match مائِل

s   What's your name? My name's Hassan.

t   United Arab Emirates, Kuwait, football

u   Damascus, Hussain, How are you?

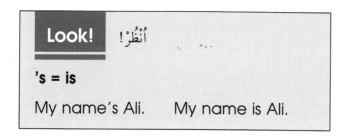

Look! اُنْظُرْ!

's = is

My name's Ali.   My name is Ali.

3 Write اُكْتُبْ

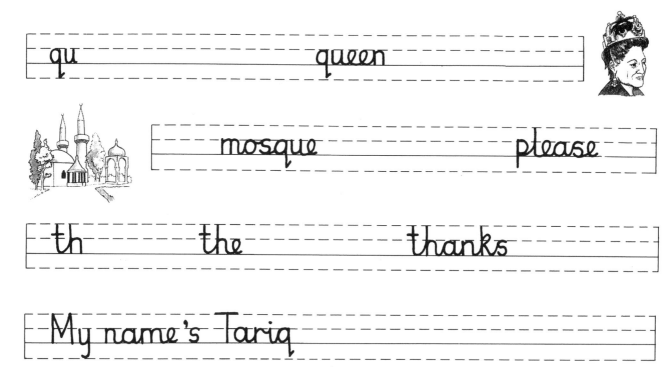

qu   queen

mosque   please

th   the   thanks

My name's Tariq

4 Match مَائِلْ

A B C D E F G H I J K L M N O P Q R S T U

s p j l a n u e r t i o d c h q m f b g k

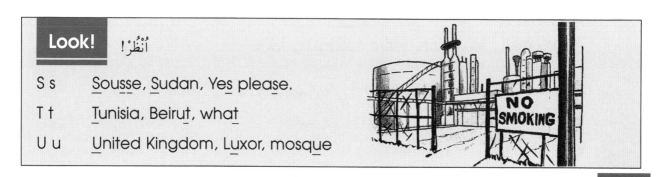

Look! اُنْظُرْ!

S s   Sousse, Sudan, Yes please.

T t   Tunisia, Beirut, what

U u   United Kingdom, Luxor, mosque

1 V W v w

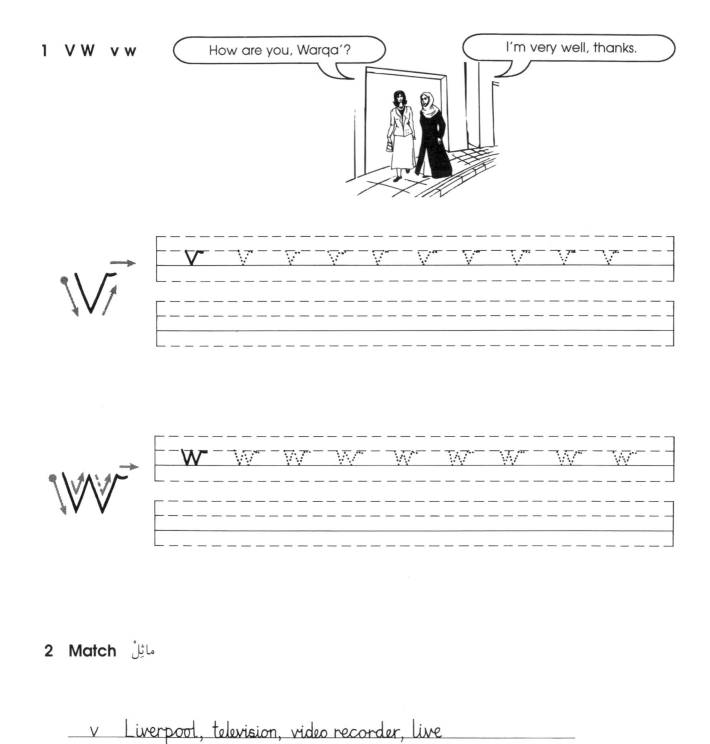

2 Match ماثِل

v Liverpool, television, video recorder, live

w Awad, Kuwait, New York, what, where, how

live   have

very well   woman

what   where

I live in Awali.

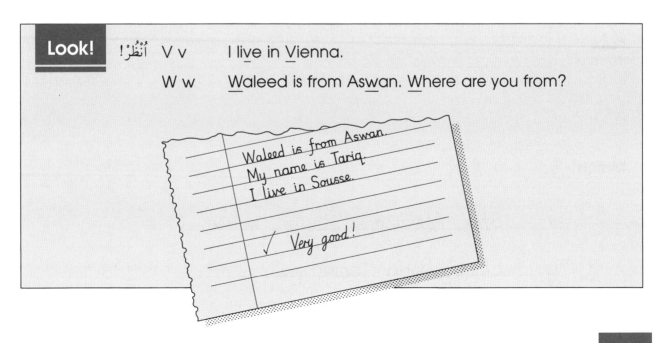

Look! اُنْظُرْ!   V v   I live in Vienna.

W w   Waleed is from Aswan. Where are you from?

Waleed is from Aswan.
My name is Tariq.
I live in Sousse.

✓ Very good!

1 X Y Z x y z

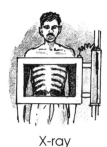

X-ray

x x x x x x x x x x

y y y y y y y y y y

z z z z z z z z z z

2 Match مائِلْ

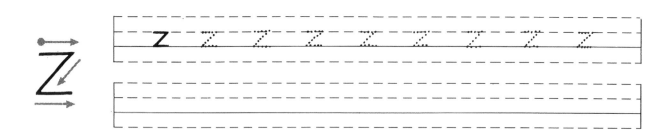

x   Sfax, Alexandria, Luxor, express

y   Libya, Syria, thank you

z   Gaza, Azraq, Fez, Hejaz

3 Write اُكْتُبْ

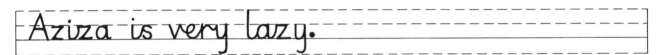

box   Luxor

yes   you   your

my   lazy

Aziza is very lazy.

Look!	اُنْظُرْ!

X x   I'm from Ale<u>x</u>andria in Egypt.

Y y   My name's <u>Y</u>acoob. Are <u>y</u>ou from <u>Y</u>emen?

Z z   A<u>z</u>i<u>z</u> and <u>Z</u>uhair live in <u>Z</u>arqa' in Jordan.

Review مُراجَعة

1 Small letters الحُروف الصَّغيرة

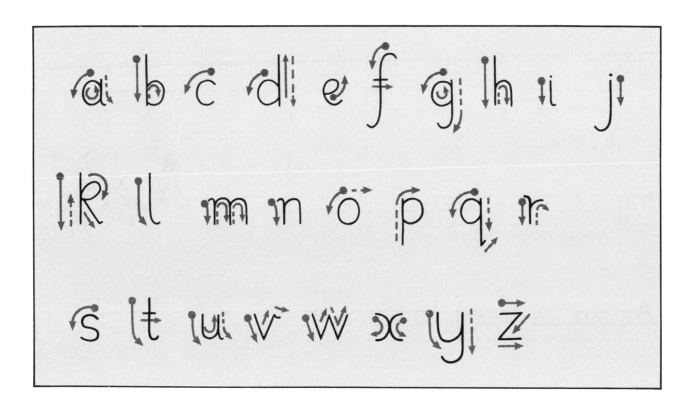

2 Match مائِلْ

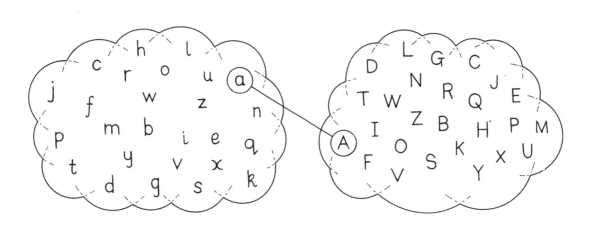

3 Write اُكْتُب

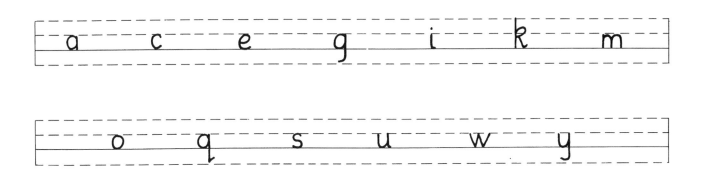

a   c   e   g   i   k   m

o   q   s   u   w   y

4 Write اُكْتُب

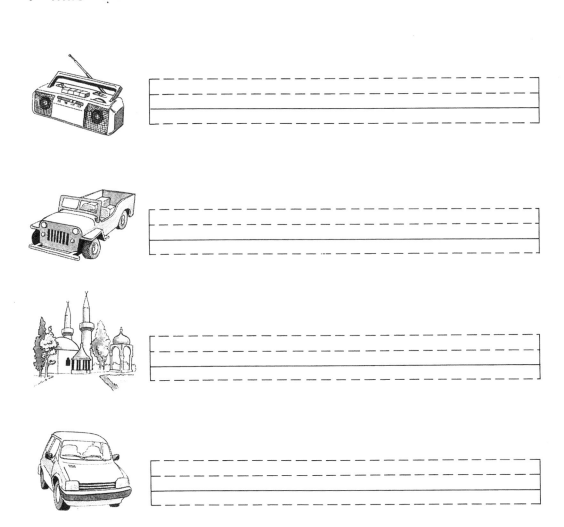

5 Listen and write اِسْتَمِعْ واكْتُبْ

WORDS كَلِمات

book	كِتاب
box	صُندوق
car	سَيّارة
fine	جَيِّد
good	جَيِّد
jeep	سَيّارة جيب
lazy	كَسول
mosque	مَسْجِد
no	لا
park	حَديقة
pen	قَلَم
please	مِن فَضْلِكَ
queen	مَلِكة
radio	راديو
thanks	شُكْرًا
the	أل
very	جِدًّا
very well	جَيِّد جِدًّا
what	ماذا
where	أَيْنَ
woman	اِمْرَأة
yes	نَعَم

What's your name? ما اسمُكَ؟

1 Names

A	Ahmed	N	Nadia
B	Badria	O	Omar
C	Charles	P	Paul
D	Daoud	Q	Qassim
E	Essa	R	Rashid
F	Fatima	S	Samira
G	Ghazi	T	Tawfiq
H	Hannan	U	Usame
I	Ibrahim	V	Victoria
J	Jameela	W	Warqa'
K	Khadijah	X	_____
L	Latifa	Y	Yacoub
M	Mona	Z	Zeinab

Write اُكْتُبْ

Ahmed

Badria

(three blank writing practice boxes)

2 Read اِقْرَأ

Hello, Mary. How are you?

I'm fine thanks. How are you?

Very well thanks.

What's your name, please?

My name's Ahmed Yacoub.

Can I have your passport, please?

3 Say قُلْ

Ask three students   اِسْأَلْ ثَلاثَةَ تَلامِيذ

A	B
What's your name, please?	**My name's . . .**

1   Name: _____   _____

2   Name: _____   _____

3   Name: _____   _____

How are you?

How are you?

I'm very well, thanks.

What's your name?

My name's Ahmed Yacoub.

Can I have your passport, please?

Lesson 27

Where are you from?

مِنْ أَيْنَ أَنْتَ؟

Welcome to Egypt.

CAIRO AIRPORT

1 Match the city with the country. مائِلْ بَيْنَ المَدينة والبَلَد

Egypt, Qatar, Syria, Bahrain, Iraq, Oman, Kuwait, United Arab Emirates, Lebanon.

	City	Country
1	Cairo	Egypt
2	Beirut	
3	Dubai	
4	Riyadh	
5	Damascus	
6	Amman	
7	Manama	
8	Baghdad	
9	Fehaheel	

2 Read اِقْرَأْ

Where are you from?

Where's that?

I'm from Fehaheel.

It's in Kuwait.

58

3 Say قُلْ

Ask three students اِسْأَلْ ثَلاثَةَ تَلاميذ

A

Where are you from?

Where's that?

B

I'm from . . .

It's in . . . .

	Name	From
1	Samira	Aswan, Egypt
2		
3		

4 Write اُكْتُبْ

Where are you from?

Where are you from?

I'm from Gabes.

Where's that?

It's in Tunisia.

5 Write أُكْتُبْ

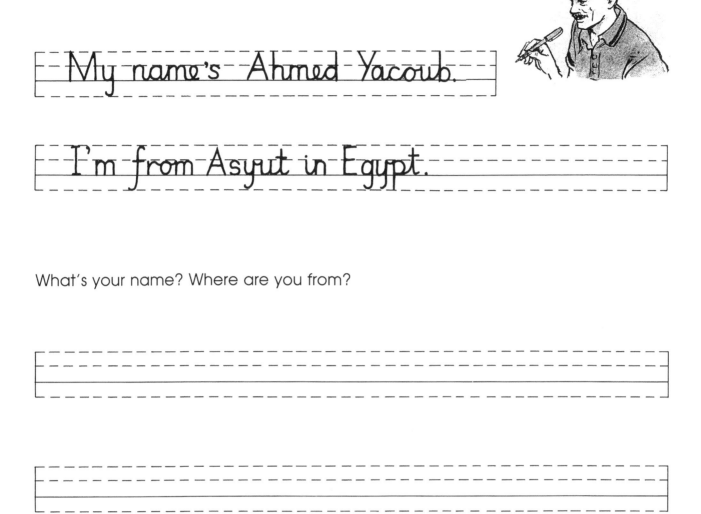

My name's Ahmed Yacoub.

I'm from Asyut in Egypt.

What's your name? Where are you from?

Numbers الأَرْقام

1 Numbers 0–10

0	zero (oh)
1	one
2	two
3	three
4	four
5	five
6	six
7	seven
8	eight
9	nine
10	ten

2 Write اُكْتُب

zero   zero

one   one

two   two

three   three

four four

five five

six six

seven seven

eight eight

nine nine

ten ten

3 Read اِقْرَأْ

What's the time, please?

It's nine o'clock.

4 Write اُكْتُبْ

What's the time? كَم السّاعَةُ؟

It's 3 o'clock

5 Say قُلْ

What's the time, please?
It's . . . o'clock.

Punctuation عَلامات التَّرقيم

1 **Look** اُنْظُرْ

exclamation mark عَلامَة التَّعَجُّب

Hello!

′s = is   question mark عَلامة الاسْتِفْهام

What's your name? ما اسْمُكَ؟

full stop

My name's Samira. اِسْمي سَميرة. نُقْطة

′m = am   comma فاصِلة

I'm very well, thank you. إنَّني بِخَيْر، والحَمْد لله

. = full stop نُقْطة
, = comma فاصِلة
? = question mark عَلامة تَعَجُّب
! = exclamation mark عَلامة اسْتِفْهام

2 **Write: . , ? ′ !** اُكْتُبْ

My name's Hussain

I'm from Abu Dhabi

Where are you from

Are you from Jeddah

Welcome

Can I have tea please

What's the time

It's six o'clock

3 Capital letters الحُروف الكَبيرة

We use capital letters at the beginning of –   نَسْتَعْمِلُ الحروف الكَبيرة في أوَّلِ

names الأسْماء

Ahmed, Fatima, Lulwa, Waleed.

cities المُدُن

Beirut, Muscat, Abu Dhabi

countries البُلْدان

Jordan, Yemen, England

We use capital letters at the beginning of a sentence.

نَسْتَعْمِل الحُروف الكَبيرة في بِدايَة الجُملة

Where are you from?
My name's Khalifa.
It's seven o'clock.
How are you?

We also write capital I – when it is alone. وأيْضًا نَكْتب الحَرْف I كَبيراً عندما يَكون وَحْدَه

I am from Bahrain.

4 Write اُكْتُبْ

Put in the capital letters. ضَع الحُروفَ الكَبيرة

a   my name's badria yousef.

b   i'm from fehaheel in kuwait.

c   what's the time?

d   are you from england?

1 Find 11 countries جِدْ ١١ بَلَدًا

```
X A L G E R I A B Y K U
D F E O Z V K J T M Q X
S L B K W S Q O L F Y B
Y S A U D I A R A B I A
R B N W J K Z D F L R A
I P O A B O M A N X A T
A C N I W Y P N R N Q X
O Y D T Z F J B E R Q O
O E U N I T E D A R A B
E M I R A T E S X B T C
Z E G Y P T D R W Q A S
V N H B A H R A I N R O
```

2 Write أُكْتُبْ

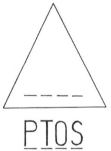

a PTOS

b ON KSIGMNO

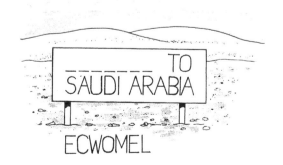

c ECWOMEL

d ON KAPIGRN

3 Numbers الأَرْقام

a reeht *three*

b net _____

c xsi _____

d vense _____

e enni _____

f noe _____

g urfo _____

h wot _____

i veif _____

j heitg _____

4 What is it? ما هي؟

a

b

c

d

e

f

g

h

1 park
2 box
3 mosque
4 ball
5 book
6 passport
7 car
8 man

5 Match the words مائِلْ بَيْنَ الكَلِمات

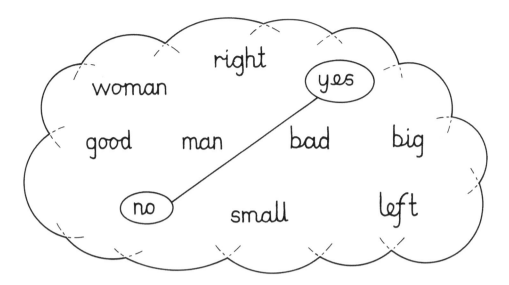

6 Cities مُدُن

Find 10 cities   جِدْ ١٠ مُدُن

a   R __ Y __ __ H

b   D __ __ A I

c   __ __ S C __ T

d   B __ __ R U __

e   C __ __ R O

f   A __ M A __

g   D __ M __ S __ __ S

h   J __ __ __ A H

i   B __ G H __ __ D

j   M __ N __ M __

Appendix

Numbers and letters

Numbers

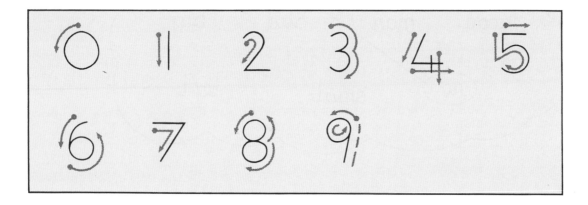

0	1	2	3	4	5	6	7	8	9	10
zero	one	two	three	four	five	six	seven	eight	nine	ten
٠	١	٢	٣	٤	٥	٦	٧	٨	٩	١٠

Capital letters

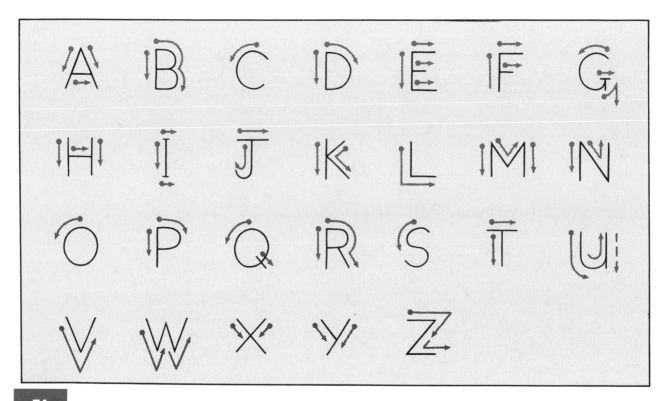

Small letters

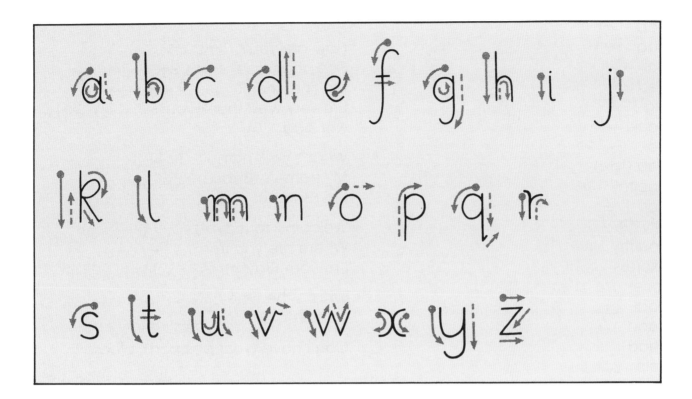

A B C D E F G H I J K L M N O P Q R S T U V W X Y Z

a b c d e f g h i j k l m n o p q r s t u v w x y z

a b c d e f g h i j k l m n o p q r s t u v w x y z

Word list قائِمة كَلِمات

bad	سَيِّئ
bag	مِحْفَظة.
ball	كُرَة
bed	سَرير
big	كَبير
book	كِتاب
box	صُنْدوق
cab (taxi)	تَكْسي
capital	عاصِمة
car	سَيّارة
city	مَدينة
country	بَلَد
express	القِطارِ السَّريع
face	وَجْه
goal	هَدَف
good	جَيِّد
head	رَأْس
help	مُساعَدة
jack	رافِعة
jacket	سُتْرَة
jeep	سَيّارة جيب
lazy	كَسول
left	يَسار
letter	حَرْف
live	حَيّ
man	رَجُل
mosque	مَسجد
number	رَقْم
park	حَديقة
passport	جَواز
pen	قَلَم
pick-up	شاحِنة
queen	مَلِكة
radio	راديو
right	مُسَجِّلة
small	صَغير
television	تلفزيون
video recorder	مُسَجِّلة فيديو
woman	إمْرَأَة
x-ray	أشِعَّة إكس

Hello.	مَرْحَبًا
How are you?	كَيْفَ حالُكَ؟
Fine, thanks.	بخَيْر والحَمْد لله
I'm fine, thank you.	إنَّني بِخَيْر والحَمْد لله
I'm very well, thank you.	إنَّني بِخَيْر والحَمْد لله
Not bad.	لا بَأْس
What's your name?	ما اسْمُكِ؟
My name's (Badria).	إسْمي بَدْرِيَّة
I'm (Badria).	أنا بَدْرِيَّة
Welcome to (Egypt).	أهْلًا بكَ في مِصْر
Where are you from?	مِنْ أَيْنَ أَنْتَ؟
I'm from (Egypt).	أنا مِن مِصْر
What's the time?	كَم الساعَةُ؟
It's seven o'clock.	إنَّها السابِعة
Can I have (your passport), please?	أعْطِني جَوازَكَ مِن فَضْلِكَ
Yes/No.	نَعَمْ / لا
Yes, please.	أَجَلْ لو سَمَحْتَ
No, thank you.	كَلّا شُكْرًا
Very good.	جَيِّدٌ جِدًّا
Stop! Go!	قِفْ! سِرْ!
No smoking.	التَّدخين مَمْنوع
No parking.	الوُقوف مَمْنوع

73

TO THE TEACHER

What are the aims of Start Writing?

1. The main aim of *Start Writing* is to introduce and practise the numbers (0-10) and the upper and lower case letters of the alphabet.

Although letters can be taught in groups according to their shape and formation, an alphabetic approach has been chosen here. Capital letters are taught first, introducing students to alphabetical order and the names of the letters. Small letters are then taught and practiced singly and within words, introducing students straight away to a simple cursive form.

The use of capital letters at the beginning of the names of people, cities and countries is also taught. Where possible, only words that students will recognize are used, e.g. common male and female Arab names and names of some Arab cities and countries. Use is also made of certain English words (jacket, passport, video), which are widely used in Arabic. Other words are chosen as they represent useful items of vocabulary.

2. A secondary aim of *Start Writing* is to present a number of everyday phrases such as "My name's …"; "What's the time?"; and "Where are you from?". This oral component gives variety to the lessons and prepares students for more general courses.

How is the book organized?

The book is divided into 30 lessons designed to give approximately one hour's teaching material per lesson. Regular review lessons are included and a word list is given in the Appendix.

How can the book be used?

Presenting numbers and letters

1. First, teachers introduce the numbers and letters on the board. Students should repeat the name of the letter after the teacher.

2. The teacher indicates how the figure is drawn, pointing out the sequence of strokes in the construction. Use the staves (dotted and solid lines) and show how the figures rest on the solid lines.

3. Students then practise tracing out the shape of the figures with their fingers. They can repeat the names of the letters to themselves.

4. Teachers refer the class to the models in the book, pointing out the numbered arrows. Students then work at their own pace, drawing the number or letter using the dotted models in the book.

5. They then continue with unguided practice on the lines provided and in their own copybooks if necessary.

Oral practice

Throughout the book phrases useful for social exchange are introduced. These phrases should be presented by

the teacher and practised by the class – in pairs where appropriate. Other items of vocabulary, including the numbers and names of the letters, should also be practised orally as they occur.

Listening practice

The teacher is required to dictate numbers, letters or words in exercises headed Listen and write. The script for each exercise is given in the notes for individual lessons.

Instructions

Instructions are given in Arabic as well as in English. However, students should become familiar with the headings – Match, Write, Say, Listen and write, etc. Teachers should use these English terms when possible.

Lesson Notes and Answer Key

LESSON 1

Aims: - to develop the left to right motor skills
- to introduce and practise the numbers 0 to 3

Language: - hello. left, right, zero, one, two, three

1 – 4 *Left to right* Students practise the left to right movements using a variety of patterns. At first they can practise by tracing patterns in the air.

5 *Numbers* Each number is presented by the teacher and practised using the steps described earlier.

LESSON 2

Aims: - to introduce and practise the numbers 4 to 6
- to review the numbers 0 to 3

Language: - telephone number, licence plate numbers, oh (for zero in telephone numbers), four, five, six

3 *Telephone numbers* Students practise reading the telephone numbers in pairs. Introduce 'oh' for 'zero' at this stage.'

4 *Listen and write* Teacher reads aloud the following numbers: 205641, 630442, 513160, 425536

LESSON 3

Aims: - to introduce and practise the numbers 7 to 9
- to review the numbers 0 to 6

Language: - plus, minus, equals, seven, eight, nine

4 *Listen and write* Teacher reads aloud the following numbers: 549320, 827661, 408059, 3718645

LESSON 4

Aims: - to introduce and practise the letters A, B and C

- to enable students to introduce themselves

- to show that personal names begin with a capital letter

Language: - Hello. I'm ….; capital letter

1 Explain the drawing showing the three people and get students to introduce themselves to one another using the phrase: "Hello. I'm …"

3 *Listen and put an X* Teacher's script: A5, A4, A3, A2, A1, B1, C2, C3, C4, B5, C6, C7, C8, B9, A9, A8, A7, A6, A5. Students join up the Xs – the shape is that of the letter 'B'.

4 *Listen and write* Dictate the following letters and numbers to the students giving them plenty of time to write. Teacher's script: B C A C B A C B – 6C, 8A, 4B, 5A, 2C, 7B

LESSON 5

Aims: - to introduce and practise the letters D, E and F

- to introduce additional Arabic names

5 *Listen and write* Teacher's script: D E B C A F – 8A 4F 3D 9E

LESSON 6

Aims: - to introduce and practise the letters G, H and I

- to enable students to exchange greetings

- to introduce the spelling aloud of names

Language: - How are you? Fine, thanks. Goal!

3 *Listen and write* Say the names and then spell them out: Fahad – F A H A D , Habiba – H A B I B A

4 *Say* Refer to the sketch of Ahmed at the beginning of the lesson. Introduce and practise the greetings with the whole group. Then let the class practise in pairs.

LESSON 7

Aims: - to introduce and practise the letters J, K and L.

- to practise the spelling of names.

4 *Listen and write* Say the names and spell them out: Khadija – K H A D I J A, Khaled – K H A L E D

LESSON 8 Review

Aims: - to review the capital letters A to L

- to enable students to say where they are from

- to introduce the names of cities and countries

- to show that cities/countries begin with capitals

Language: - I'm from ….., flight number

1 and 2 *Match* Use the examples to show that the name of a country begins with a capital letter. Teach the phrase – "I'm

from …" – and get students to say where they are from as a group or in pairs. ("Where are you from?" is introduced later but could be brought in at this stage.)

4 *Listen and write* Read out the names of the places and then spell them: Jeddah – J E D D A H, Khafji – K H A F J I

5 *Listen and write* Read out the following cities and flight numbers: Damascus – AF 417, Cairo – BA 328, Jeddah

– JB 095, Kuwait – KL 632, Bahrain – GF – 403. Students complete the table.

LESSON 9

Aims: - to introduce and practise the letters M, N and O

- to further practise introductions

- to teach the sounds of the letters

Language: - My name's ….; Are you OK? No.

3 *Say* Introduce the greeting, "Hello. My name's ,,,," and practise as a group and in pairs.
Students can be given (or choose) names of famous people.

4 *Say* Students should repeat the letters in sound groups after the teacher.

LESSON 10

Aims: - to introduce and practise the letters P, Q and R

- to point out the distinction between the sound of the letters P and B

Language: - please, come in

1 Use the sketch to introduce the phrase – "Please, come in." Practise the pronunciation of "please".

5 *Say* Practise the sounds of the letters P and B and M and N. Then dictate the following letters: 1. B A P C O (the name of Bahrain's oil company), 2. Manama M A N A M A

LESSON 11

Aims: - to introduce and practise the letters S, T and U

- to further practise introductions

Language: - gulf, hotel, stop, go

4 *Say* Students practise the introductions – "My name's ….., I'm from …." – as a group and in pairs. They can choose the names of famous people.

5 *Listen and write* Teacher's script: Gulf Hotel – G U L F H O T E L. Introduce the words 'gulf' and 'hotel'. Refer to the cartoons. Teach the full name – 'United Arab Emirates'. Practise the words 'stop' and 'go'.

LESSON 12

Aims: - to introduce and practise the letters V and W

- to review alphabetical order of the letters A to W

Language: - Welcome to …., TV, VIP, airport

3 *Listen and write* Teacher's script: Wadi Kabir – W A D I K A B I R , Kuwait – K U W A I T

Use the airport scene at the end of the lesson to act out similar exchanges in pairs using the phrases – "My name's …" , "I'm …. Welcome to …." Students can take turns at being the visitor.

LESSON 13

Aims: - to introduce and practise the letters X, Y and Z

      - to review the alphabetical order

Language: - Yes, please. No, thank you. Tea. Fax, Exit

4 *Listen and write* Teacher's script: Nizwa – N I Z W A, Zanzibar – Z A N Z I B A R, Yasser – Y A S S E R, Fax – F A X, Exit – E X I T

Use the drawing of the three women to teach the responses - "Yes, please." and "No, thank you." Practise the rising intonation of "Tea?" and act out similar exchanges with the class. Items such as 'coffee' and 'water' could be introduced.

LESSON 14 Review

Aims: - to review all the capital letters and the numbers 0 to 9

      - to practise the sounds of the capital letters by group

Language: - jacket, car

4 *What is it?* Get students into pairs. The first student reads the letters and numbers to their partner who draws Xs on the diagram. The sketch resembles a jacket.

5 *What is it?* Students reverse roles and the second student reads out the letters and numbers to the first student. The diagram represents a car.

LESSON 15

Aims: - to introduce and practise the small letters a, b and c

      - to match the form of the capital letters with that of the small letters

Language: - taxi, cab, small letter

2 *Match* A recognition exercise using cursive script. Students underline all the examples of the small letter in the given words.

Look! Draw the students' attention to the printed form of the capital and small letters. Note their positions in the words.

LESSON 16

Aims: - to introduce and practise the small letters d, e and f

Language: - bed, bad, face

LESSON 17

Aims: - to introduce and practise the small letters g, h and i. Note the 'hard' pronunciation of 'g' at the beginning of 'garage'; and the 'soft' pronunciation in 'Algeria' and 'George'.

Language: - big, bad, head, garage, happy

LESSON 18

Aims: - to introduce and practise the small letters j, k and l.

Language: - help, jack, ball, jeep, small letter, capital letter

LESSON 19 Review

Aims: - to review the small letters a to l

      - to match the letters with the capital letters

      - to practise exchanging greetings

Language: - And you? I'm fine.

5 *Say* Practise the exchange with the class before asking them to do similar exchanges in pairs. (The responses "very well" and "not bad" are introduced later but could be brought in at this point.)

LESSON 20

Aims: - to introduce and practise the small letters m, n and o

Language: - am ('m), man, not, not bad, book, good Point out the form – am – and its contraction – 'm . Demonstrate the pronunciation of "I'm fine", and "I am fine." Try to get the students to use the contracted form in speech.

LESSON 21

Aims: - to introduce and practise the small letters p, q and r

Language: - pen, radio, park, pick-up. No parking. Happy birthday.

Teach the phrases 'no parking' and 'happy birthday'. Pay attention to pronunciation.

LESSON 22

Aims: - to introduce and practise the small letters s, t and u

Language: - is ('s), queen, mosque, please. No smoking.

Point out the verb is and its contraction, 's. Demonstrate the difference in pronunciation with the practice sentences, "My name's Ali", "My name is Ali."

Use the sketch of the refinery to teach and practise the phrases, "no smoking" with the class.

LESSON 23

Aims: - to introduce and practise the small letters v and w

      - to further practise the exchange of greetings

Language: - live, have, very well, very good, woman, what, where. I live ....., Where are you from?

Use the sketch at the beginning of the lesson to teach the response, "I'm very well, thanks." Students can practise the exchange in pairs.

LESSON 24

Aims: - to introduce and practise the small letters x, y and z

Language: - box, lazy, express

LESSON 25 Review

Aims: - to review all the small letters

- to match the small letters with the appropriate capital letters

- to review some of the vocabulary introduced so far

5 *Listen and write* Students should write the following names of countries and people in cursive script using small and capital letters as appropriate. Give examples on the board first to show what is required. Teacher's script: Muscat – M U S C A T, Salalah – S A L A L A H, Yasmin – Y A S M I N, Abdul Aziz – A B D U L A Z I Z.

LESSON 26 What's your name?

Aims: - to review the Arabic names introduced so far

- to review social exchanges

Language: - What's your name, please? Can I have your passport?

2 *Read* Practise the two exchanges with the class. The students then practise the exchanges in pairs.

3 *Say* Students ask three other students in the class for their names and write down the answers. They should check for spelling if necessary (Teach: "How do you spell that?"). Students should give two names (e.g. first name and family name).

LESSON 27 Where are you from?

Aims: - to review cities and countries

- to practise exchanges about place of origin

Language: - Where are you from? I'm from ..... Where's that? It's in ...... , city, country

3 *Say* Practise the questions, "Where are you from?", "Where's that?" and the responses. Students then ask the questions to three others and write the replies in the spaces.

LESSON 28 Numbers

Aims: - to review the numbers 0 to 9 and introduce the number 10

- to introduce telling the time

Language: - ten, What's the time, please? It's ......o'clock.

3 *Read* Teach the question, "What's the time?" and the response, "It's nine o'clock." with the whole class. Use clocks drawn on the board to extend the practice to include all the numbers up to ten. (Eleven and twelve could be added at this point.)

5 *Say* Students can work in pairs, taking turns to ask the time.

LESSON 29 Punctuation

Aims: - to introduce the punctuation symbols and basic rules for their use

- to review the rules for the use of capital letters

Language: - full stop (period), comma, question mark, exclamation mark

1 *Look* Point out the punctuation marks and give then their English names. Note that 'full stop' is called 'period' in American English. Indicate the position of the comma before "thank you" and also "please".

2 *Write Answer key:*

a My name's Hussain.   b I'm from Abu Dhabi.

c Where are you from?   d Are you from Jeddah?

e Welcome!   f Can I have tea, please?

g What's the time?   h It's six o'clock.

4 *Write Answer key:*

a My name's Badria Yousef. b I'm from Fahaheel in Kuwait.

c What's the time?   d Are you from England?

LESSON 30

Aims: - to review the language of the whole course through word puzzles

Answer key:

1 *Find 11 countries*

Horizontal: Algeria, Saudi Arabia, United Arab Emirates, Egypt, Bahrain

Vertical: Syria, Yemen, Lebanon, Kuwait, Jordan, Qatar

2 *Write*

a STOP, b NO SMOKING, c WELCOME, d NO PARKING

4 *What is it?*

a book, b man, c car, d ball, e park, f mosque, g passport, h box

5 *Match the words*

yes/no, man/woman, big/small, good/bad, left/right

6 *Cities*

a Riyadh, b Dubai, c Muscat, d Beirut, e Cairo, f Amman, g Damascus, h Jeddah, I Baghdad, j Manama